Europe

COLORING BOOK

Jamon

SPAIN

Hola!

Dali

Madrid

Paella

Olive

Corrida

toreador

Bandurria

Flamenco

S. PIETRO IN MONTORIO

BRAMANTE ARCHITETTO

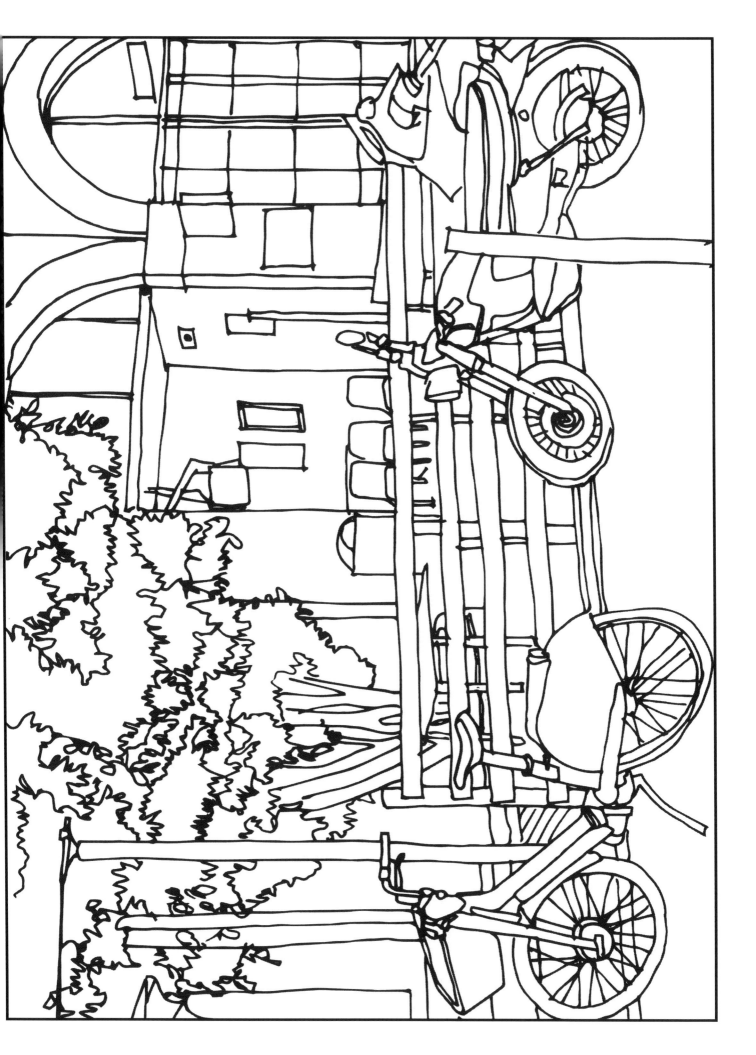

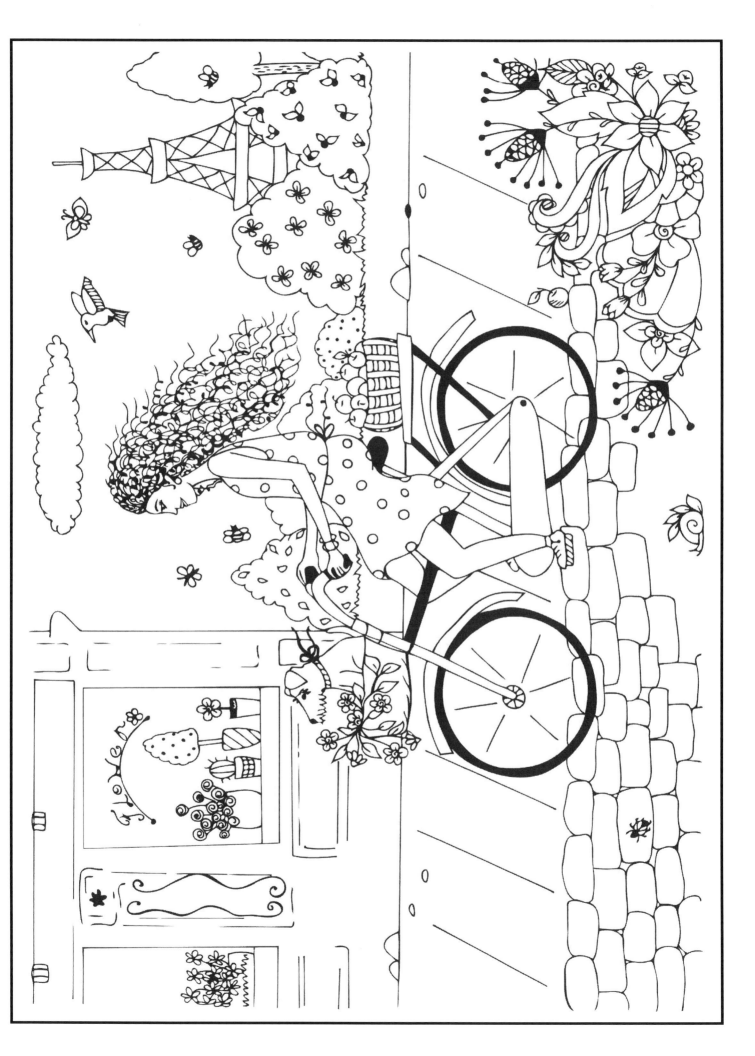

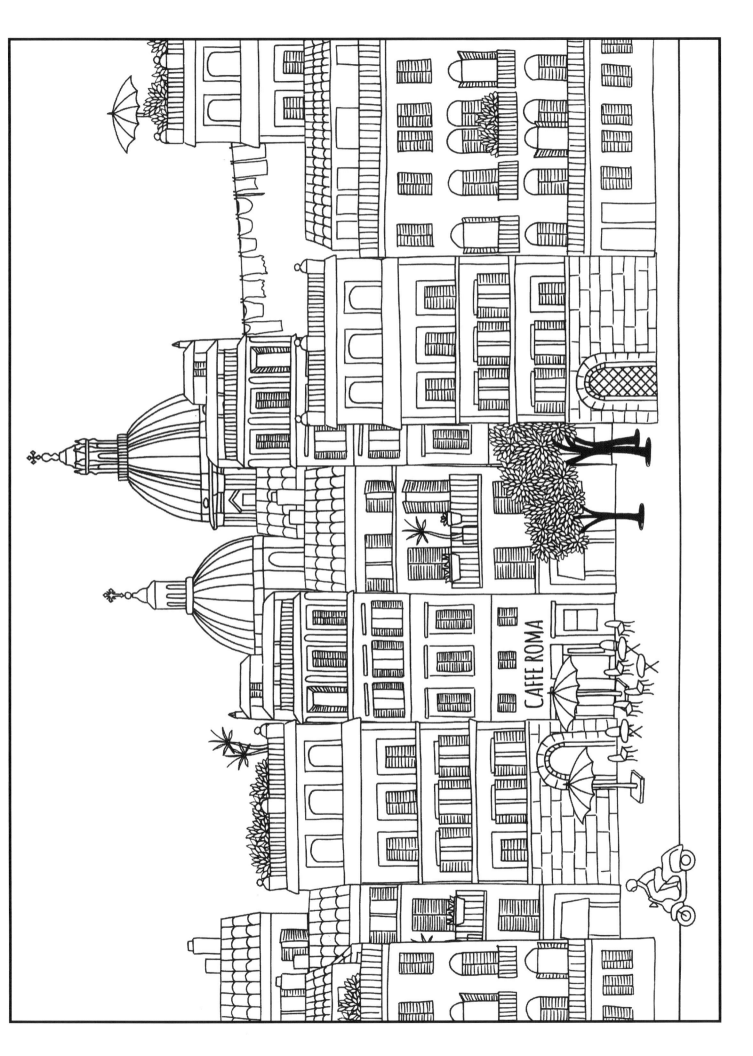

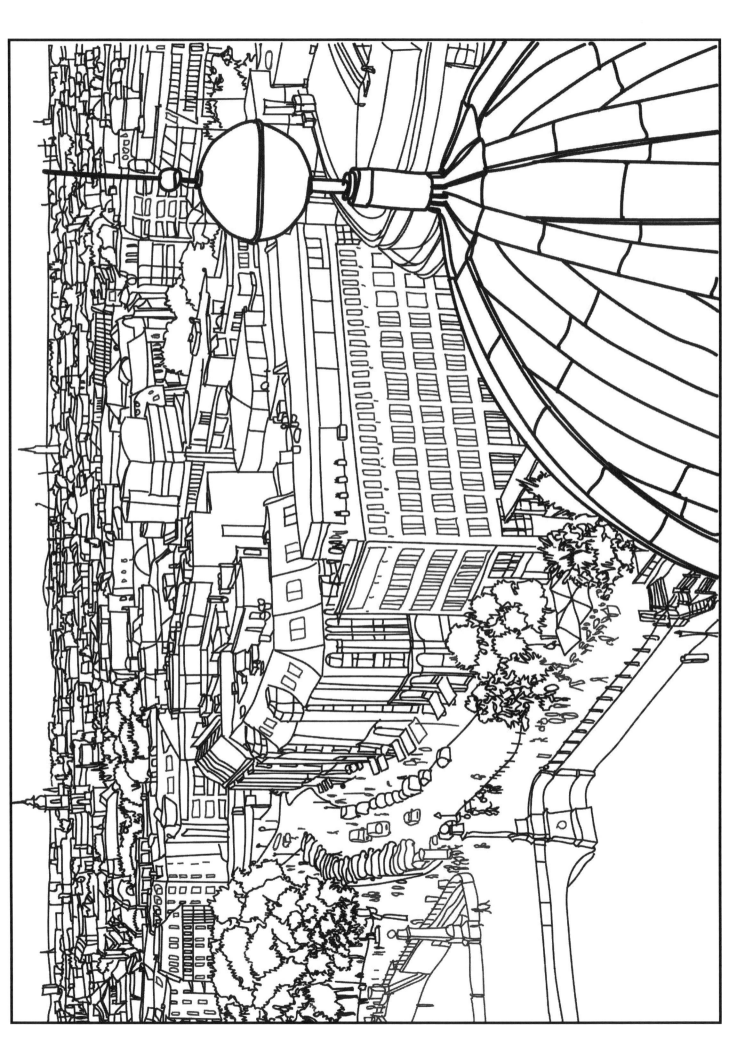

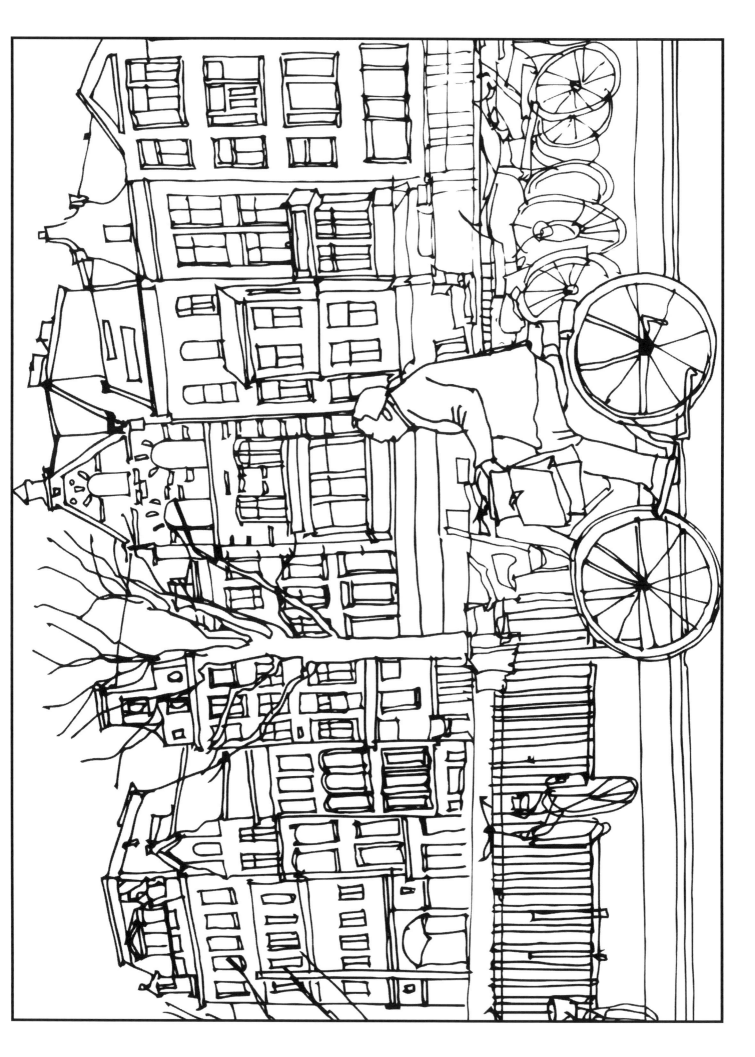

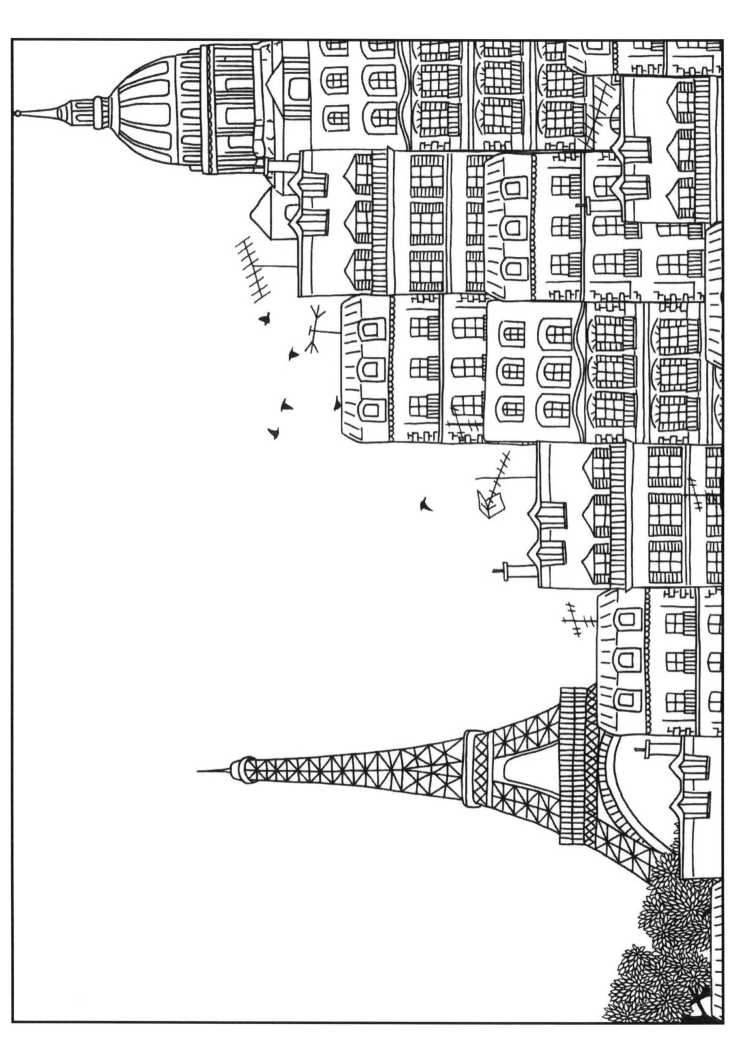

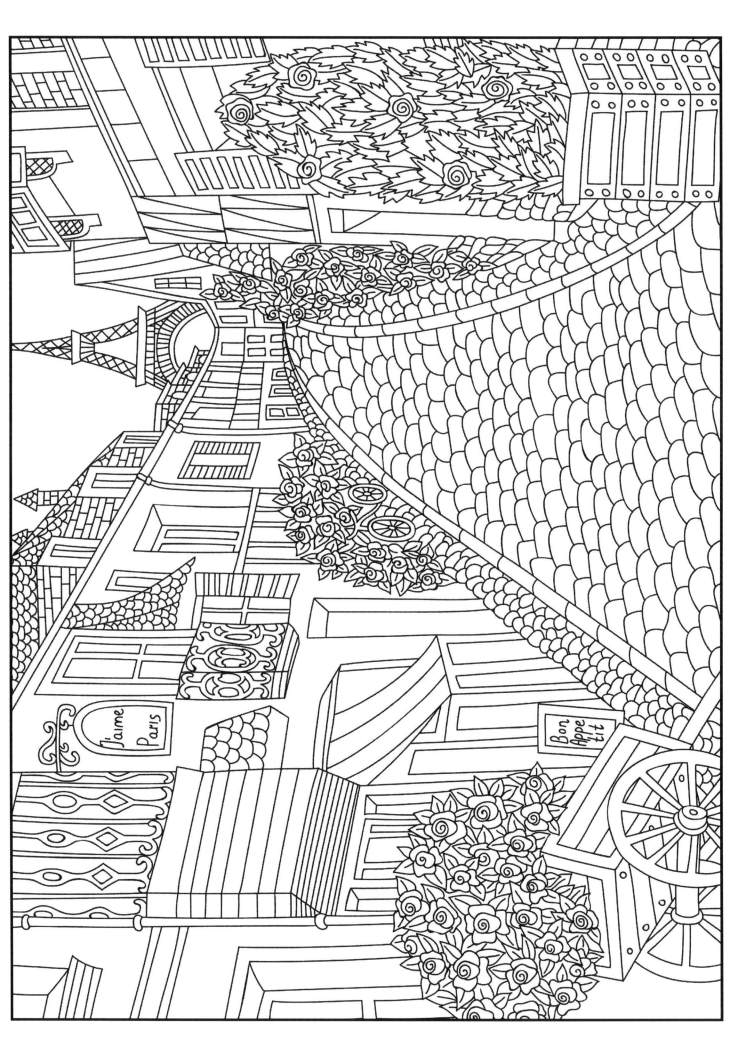

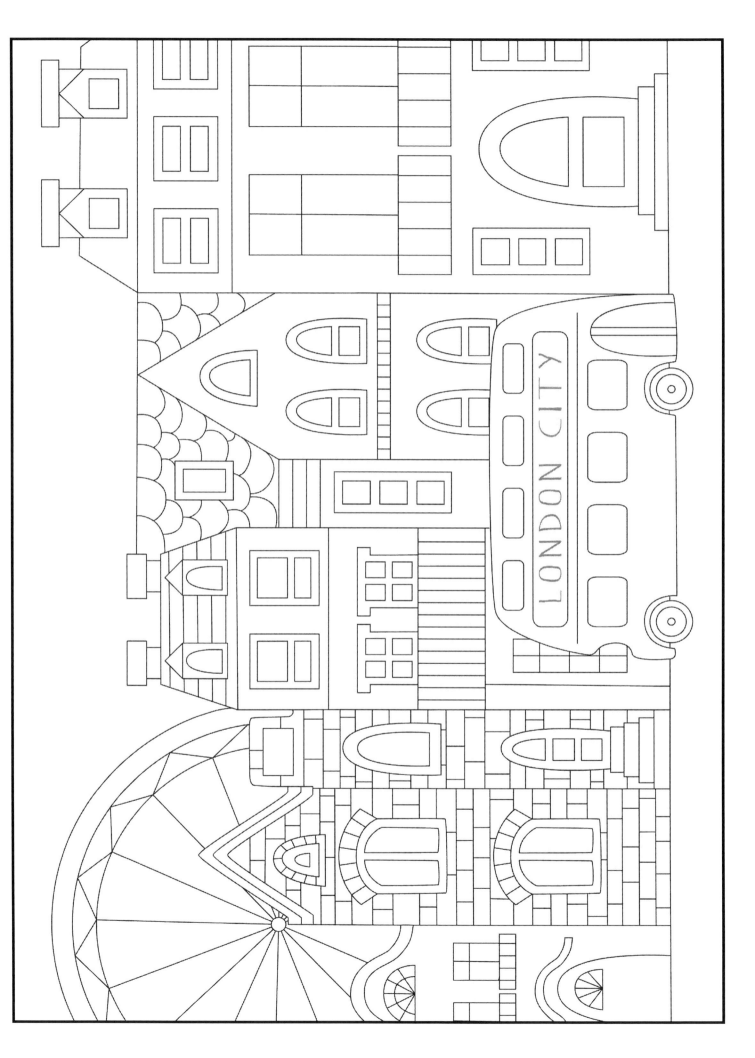

Made in the USA
Columbia, SC
05 December 2020